THE

STORY

OF

MICHELANGELO'S

PIETÀ

OFFICIAL EDITION
Vatican Pavilion—New York World's Fair, Inc.

by Irving Stone

BIOGRAPHICAL NOVELS

Lust for Life (Vincent Van Gogh)
Immortal Wife (Jessie Benton Fremont)
Adversary in the House (Eugene V. Debs)
The Passionate Journey (John Noble)
The President's Lady (Rachel Jackson)
Love Is Eternal (Mary Todd Lincoln)
The Agony and the Ecstasy (Michelangelo)

BIOGRAPHIES

Sailor on Horseback (Jack London)
They Also Ran (Defeated Presidential Candidates)
Clarence Darrow for the Defense
Earl Warren

HISTORY

Men to Match My Mountains

NOVELS

Pageant of Youth
False Witness

BELLES-LETTRES

We Speak for Ourselves (A Self-Portrait of America)

WITH JEAN STONE

Dear Theo *and* I, Michelangelo, Sculptor
(*Autobiographies through letters*)

COLLECTED

The Irving Stone Reader

THE
STORY
OF
MICHELANGELO'S
PIETÀ

BY

IRVING STONE

Doubleday & Company, Inc.
Garden City, New York
1964

The author wishes to acknowledge his indebtedness to Doubleday & Company, Inc., for the use of material from *The Agony and the Ecstasy;* to the New York *Times Magazine* for the use of material from " 'Improbable' Story of the Pietà" (copyright © 1962 by the New York Times Company. Reprinted by permission); and to the *Reader's Digest* for the release of reprint rights to this article. The author also wishes to thank John J. Delaney of Doubleday for his editorial assistance.

COVER PHOTOGRAPH COURTESY OF ALINARI, ART REFERENCE BUREAU

CONTENTS

THE

STORY

OF

MICHELANGELO'S

PIETÀ

PROLOGUE

In 1492, while Michelangelo was living in the Medici Palace, carving his Battle of the Centaurs, a fellow Italian, Christopher Columbus, discovered the islands lying off the east coast of America. In 1497, while Michelangelo was beginning to design the Pietà, one of his future neighbors in the Piazza Ognissanti in Florence, Amerigo Vespucci, set foot, or so he claimed, on the North American continent.

In 1962 Pope John XXIII, at the request of Cardinal Spellman, gave permission for the most famous and beloved of Michelangelo's religious sculptures, the Pietà, to be brought to New York for the World's Fair in 1964. This is the first time the Pietà has left the walls of St. Peter's since the sculptor placed it there himself. It is also the first time that a major Michelangelo marble carving has been seen in the United States.

It is pleasant to think that a country just discovered to Europe when Michelangelo was carving his Pietà, and a people not yet born, now have the opportunity to see the artist's supreme religious creation on the 400th anniversary of his death.

It is not unlikely that Michelangelo, too, might have been happy about this altogether unpredictable occasion.

BACKGROUND

Michelangelo, born March 6, 1475, was the second of five sons of the Buonarroti, a once wealthy Florentine family which had established its fortune in 1260. However, Michelangelo's grandfather and granduncle had lost their considerable patrimony by poor real estate buys and money-changing deals.

Though the Buonarroti bragged of having paid their taxes in Florence for three hundred years, they were one of the most art-blind and art-niggardly families in Tuscan history, never acquiring art works for themselves or endowing a chapel to contain a Giotto, Cimabue, Pisano, Orcagna, Masaccio or Botticelli, as did almost all of Italy's first families.

Michelangelo began to draw while still a child, played hooky from Master Urbino's School of Grammar to sketch from the Masaccios in the Brancacci Chapel of the Church of the Carmine. Desolate because the last of the great school of Tuscan sculptors—Donatello, Luca della Robbia, Desiderio da Settignano, Mino da Fiesole —had either died or moved away, he apprenticed himself to Ghirlandaio, the superb muralist of Santa Maria Novella, to learn the fundamentals of art.

After a year, in 1489, Lorenzo de Medici, *Il Mag-*

nifico, opened a sculpture garden, with the very old sculptor Bertoldo as master, to bring back to life the disappearing art of marble carving. Here Michelangelo spent two years, working and learning prodigiously; and here his skill in carving a faun, and the intensity of his passion for sculpture, awakened *Il Magnifico's* interest. He was invited to move into the Medici Palace as a son of the family, joining young Giovanni, later Pope Leo X, and Cousin Giulio, later Pope Clement VII. Here, too, he was given an education at the hands of Lorenzo's Plato Academy: Poliziano, Landino, Ficino, Pico della Mirandola, four of the most brilliant minds in Europe.

Though his father, Lodovico Buonarroti, bitterly opposed his becoming a sculptor, since an artist had only the lowly status of an artisan in Tuscan society, Michelangelo spent the happiest years of his life in the Medici school, carving at the age of sixteen the Madonna of the Stairs, a bas-relief of such power that it is still fresh and deeply moving today; and at seventeen sculpting the Battle of the Centaurs, so filled with the force and grace of the male body that it presaged the David in marble and the Sistine Chapel vault in paint.

Il Magnifico died in 1492, when Michelangelo was seventeen; the Medici Palace was sacked by Florentines angered by the arrogance of Lorenzo's son Pietro; and Michelangelo imagined he, too, had to flee his native city. He stayed in Bologna for a year, where through the intercession of Gianfrancesco Aldovrandi, whom Michelangelo had met in the Medici Palace, he secured a commission to complete the Dell'Arca tomb in the Church of San Domenico, with a St. Proculus, a St. Petronius and an Angel with Candlestick, interesting figures of a sound, conventional craftsmanship.

Back in Florence without patron or money, he secured a small commission for a young St. John from some Medici cousins. Then he was adrift again. He carved a small Cupid to keep his hand in. The Medici cousins said that if he buried the Cupid in the ground for a time, they could sell it in Rome as an antiquity. Michelangelo agreed, and the carving was sold for 200 ducats.

However, the purchaser, the astute Cardinal Riario, detected the fraud and had Michelangelo brought to Rome—not to punish the young miscreant but to employ him, since the Cupid had shown promise. Michelangelo, now twenty-one and on fire to put hammer and chisel to marble, was kept dangling by Cardinal Riario for a whole year because the Cardinal could not make up his mind what theme he wanted his young sculptor to pursue.

Desperate, with no way to practice his craft, Michelangelo left the Cardinal's palace and was preparing to return to Florence in defeat when he met Jacopo Galli, a Roman banker whose family had been collecting antique sculptures for generations. Galli sensed Michelangelo's talent, took him into his family home and commissioned him to carve a Bacchus.

In his first life-size sculpture, Michelangelo designed with a staggering boldness of invention. A dangerously outstretched arm of the tipsy Bacchus, a sensual flesh, the high polish of the skin, covering the most authentic anatomical structure yet seen in Europe (he had spent months illegally dissecting corpses in the hospital of Florence's Santo Spirito), would make the figure more forthrightly pagan than any of the Greek antiquities to be seen in Rome.

Just how the Pietà, Michelangelo's most sacred work,

arose out of the Bacchus, his most profane, is one of those mysteries that can be answered in terms of faith alone. Among Jacopo Galli's friends was the French Cardinal Groslaye of San Dionigi, an aged, intensely spiritual Benedictine who lived a blameless life in the midst of Rome's corruption. The Cardinal had secured permission from the Pope to leave behind him something of beauty in Rome. He wanted a sculpture carved for the Chapel of the Kings of France in the Basilica of St. Peter's. The concept for a Pietà appears to have originated in Michelangelo's mind, but it was enthusiastically approved by the Cardinal.

Michelangelo began the work in 1498 and completed it toward the end of 1499, when he was only twenty-four years old, an age at which earlier generations of Tuscan stone carvers had been still struggling to complete their apprenticeship. Though he lived to be almost ninety, and carved sculptures of staggering force and beauty, such as the David, Moses, Dusk and Dawn, the Medici Madonna, the Giant called Atlas, there are many who feel that he never again achieved the flawless beauty or depth of compassion to be found in the Pietà.

The story behind the carving is filled with improbabilities.

THE STORY

I.

Jacopo Galli was fascinated with Michelangelo's drawing of the Bacchus. Now that he had the banker's approval, the sculptor immersed himself completely in the task of creating a living, pulsing Bacchus from the white, translucent marble. The weeks and months of uninterrupted carving flowed by in a continuous stream. The winter was mild, he did not have to put back the roof of the shed; when the weather was sharp he wore his wool hat with its earmuffs, and a warm tunic. Thoughts, feelings, perceptions often came in a flash as the Bacchus and Satyr began to emerge, but to express these ideas in marble took days and weeks. Inside himself he had to grow as his sculpture grew and matured. The unfinished block haunted him at every hour of the night and day. It would be dangerous to release the bowl and the flexed knee in space; he would have to keep a webbing of marble between the outstretched bowl and forearm, between the knee and elbow, between the base and knee to give them support while he dug deeper. Now he was chiseling the side plane, the face and head, part of the neck and curls of grapes, now the depth of the left shoulder, thigh and calf. At the rear he evolved the Satyr, the stump he was sitting on, the grapes he was eating, the tiger cloth tying the two figures together. It was the most complicated piece he had yet attempted. He turned the Satyr's head, arms and grapes adroitly to the Bacchus's arm, yet ran out of marble.

Because he would take no time off for friends or rest or social life, his friend Balducci accused him of trying to escape the world by fleeing into marble. He admitted to his friend that he was half right: the sculptor carries into the marble the vision of a more luminous world than the one that surrounds him. But the artist was not in flight; he was in pursuit. He was trying with all his might to overtake a vision. Did God really rest on the seventh day? In the cool of that long afternoon, when He was refreshed, might He not have asked Himself, "Whom have I on earth to speak for Me? I had best create another species, one apart. I will call him 'artist.' His will be the task to bring meaning and beauty to the world."

He finally acceded to Balducci's importuning that he watch some of the Roman spectacles, and went with him to Mount Testaccio to see Rome celebrate carnival before Lent.

When Michelangelo returned to the house he found the French Cardinal Groslaye of San Dionigi there. A wisp of a man in an elegantly trimmed white beard and scarlet cassock who had begun his religious life as a Benedictine monk and, beloved by Charles VIII for his devotion and learning, he had been made a cardinal through the King's intervention. He lived the same devout life in Rome that he had in the Benedictine monasteries, continuing his studies of the Church Fathers, on whom he was an authority.

Galli broke a self-imposed rule by asking if they

might take the cardinal out to the workshop to see the Bacchus. Michelangelo could not refuse. In the lamplighted shed Michelangelo explained that he was working all around the figure simultaneously, to keep the forms advancing in the same stage of development. He showed how, in order to open the space between the two legs, and between the left arm and torso, he worked the front and then the back of the block, continuously making the marble web thinner and thinner. As the Cardinal of San Dionigi watched, he picked up a point and demonstrated the extremely light tapping required for the breakthrough, then used an *ugnetto* to remove the rest of the web, freeing the limbs.

"But how do you achieve in a half-finished figure this sense of throbbing vitality? I can feel the blood and muscle under your marble skin. It is good to see new marble masters arising."

A few days later a servant brought a note to the workshed from Galli. *"Won't you join Groslaye and myself for supper tonight?"*

Michelangelo quit work at sundown, went to the baths close by, steamed the marble dust out of his pores, put on a fresh shirt and hose, brushed his hair forward over his brow. Signora Galli served a light supper, for the cardinal still followed the disciplines of his early years, ate no meat, and touched all foods sparingly. His fading eyes gleamed in the candlelight as he turned to Michelangelo.

"You know, my son, I am growing old. I must leave something behind me, something of singular beauty to add to the beauties of Rome. A tribute from France, from Charles VIII and my humble self. I have secured permission from the Pope to dedicate a sculpture in the Chapel of the Kings of France in St. Peter's. There is a niche that will take a life-size sculpture."

Michelangelo had not touched any of Galli's excellent Trebbiano wine, but he felt as though he had drunk heavily on a warm afternoon. A sculpture for St. Peter's, the oldest and most sacred basilica in Christendom, built over the tomb of St. Peter! Could it be possible that the French cardinal would choose him? But from what? The little Cupid? The still nascent Bacchus in his workshed?

By the time he brought his senses back to the table, the conversation had changed. The cardinal was telling Jacopo Galli of the writings of two unorthodox post-Nicene Fathers. Then the cardinal's carriage came for him. He bade Michelangelo a pleasant good night.

That Sunday Michelangelo went to mass in St. Peter's to see the Chapel of the Kings of France and the niche about which the Cardinal of San Dionigi had talked. He climbed the thirty-five stairs of marble and porphyry leading up to the basilica, crossed the atrium, passed the center fountain surrounded by porphyry columns and stood at the base of the Carlovingian bell tower, aghast at the dilapidated condition of St. Peter's, which was leaning sharply to the left. Inside he found the Chapel of the Kings of France to be of modest size, dark, the main light coming from small windows up near the roof, the only ornamentation some sarcophagi borrowed from pagan and early Christian tombs, and a wooden crucifix in a niche on the side. He measured with his eye the vacant niche on the opposite wall, disappointed to find it so deep that a statue would be seen only from the front.

It was seven days before Galli brought up the subject again.

"You know, Michelangelo, this commission of the Cardinal of San Dionigi's could be the most important since Pollaiuolo was assigned to do a tomb for Sixtus IV."

Michelangelo's heart began to pound. "What are my chances?"

Galli counted on his long supple fingers as on an abacus that reckoned artistic probability.

"First, I must convince the cardinal that you are the best sculptor in Rome. Second, you must conceive a theme that will inspire him. Third, we must secure a signed contract."

"It would have to be a spiritual theme?"

"Not because Groslaye is a member of the Church, but because he is a deeply spiritual man. He has lived in Rome for three years in such a state of grace that he literally has not seen and does not know the depravity of the city."

"Is it innocence? Or blindness?"

"Could we say that it is faith? If a man is as pure in heart as the Cardinal of San Dionigi, he walks with God's hand on his shoulder; he sees beyond present evil to the Church Eternal."

"Can I create a marble that would have the hand of God on it?"

Galli shook his leonine head.

"That is a problem you must wrestle with yourself."

To carve decay all day, and at the same time conceive a devout theme, seemed an impossible undertaking. Yet he knew very soon that his theme would be a Pietà: Pity, Sorrow. He had wanted to do a Pietà ever since he had completed his Madonna and Child: for just as the Madonna and Child was the beginning, the Pietà was the end, the preordained conclusion of everything that Mary had decided in that fateful hour God had allotted to her. Now, thirty-three years later, her Son was again on her lap, having completed His journey.

Galli was intrigued with his thinking, took him to the Cardinal of San Dionigi's palace, where they waited for the cardinal to complete the five daily hours of prayer and offices required of every Benedictine. The three men sat in the open loggia, facing the Via Recta, with a painted Annunciation behind them. The cardinal was ashen after his long devotions. Michelangelo's practiced eye could perceive almost no body lines beneath his robe. But when the cardinal heard about the Pietà his eyes sparkled.

"What about the marble, Michelangelo? Could you find such a perfect piece as you speak of, here in Rome?"

"I think not, Your Grace. A column, yes; but an oblong block that is wider than it is tall, and cut deep, that I have not seen."

"Then we must turn to Carrara. I shall write to the brothers in Lucca, asking for aid. If they cannot find what we need you must go yourself to the quarries and find our marble."

Michelangelo bounded out of his chair.

"Did you know, Father, that the higher one quarries, the purer white the marble becomes? No earth stains, no pressure to make holes or hollows. If we could quarry at the peak of Monte Sagro, there we would find the supreme block."

On the way home Galli said, "You must go to Carrara at once. I will advance the expenses for your trip."

"I can't."

"Why not?"

"I must finish the Bacchus," he replied.

"The Bacchus can wait. The cardinal can't. One day soon God will rest His hand just a trifle more heavily on his shoulder, and Groslaye will go to heaven. From heaven he cannot commission a Pietà."

"That is true. But I cannot stop work now," Michelangelo insisted stubbornly.

"I release you from our agreement. When you have finished the Pietà you will come back to the Bacchus."

"For me there is no coming back. The sculpture is growing complete in my mind. I must finish it now to get it perfect."

"I'm always amazed to find a romantic in affairs of practical business." Galli sighed. "I shan't burden the cardinal with the details of your orthodoxy."

"Until the Bacchus is completed the Pietà cannot begin."

As the spring of 1498 advanced, Michelangelo became impatient to be finished with the Bacchus. He had
only indicated the position of the forehead, nose, mouth,
wanting to let the rest of the figure suggest the expression on the face. Now he completed the features, the
expression dazed as the Bacchus stared at the cup of
wine; the eyes bulging, the mouth opened greedily. For
the grapes he used a drill, making each one round and
juice-laden. To achieve the hair on the Satyr's goat legs
he sliced the rough-edged marble with a fully rounded
chisel which brought out the rhythmic play of curls,
each tuft designed separately.

There was left two months of polishing to get the
glowing flesh effects he wanted. Though this work involved infinite care and precision, it was technical in
nature and used only that part of him which was the
craftsman. It left his mind free during the warm spring
hours to reflect on the Pietà and its meaning. In the cool
of the evenings he began searching for this last moment
that mother and son would spend together.

He asked Jacopo Galli if he could now complete a
contract with the Cardinal of San Dionigi. Galli explained that the cardinal's monastery in Lucca had al-

ready ordered a block to Michelangelo's dimensions. The block had been cut, but the quarry at Carrara had refused to ship it to Rome before being paid. The monastery at Lucca had in turn refused to pay until the cardinal approved the block. The quarry had grown tired of holding it and had sold it to a buying agent.

That night Michelangelo wrote an agreement which he thought would be fair to himself and to the Cardinal of San Dionigi. Galli read it without expression, said he would take it to his bank and put it in a safe place.

By the end of summer the Bacchus was finished. Galli was overjoyed with his statue.

One night soon after, Galli brought home a contract he himself had written between Michelangelo and the Cardinal of San Dionigi, and which the cardinal had signed. In it Michelangelo found himself called *maestro* for the first time; but he was also described as *statuario*, statue maker, which was deflating. For the sum of four hundred and fifty ducats in papal gold he agreed to make a Pietà of marble, one hundred and fifty ducats to be paid as he began, and a hundred ducats every fourth month. By the end of a year the statue was to be completed. In addition to guaranteeing the cardinal's payments to Michelangelo, Galli had written:

I, Jacopo Galli, do promise that the work will be more beautiful than any work in marble to be seen in Rome today, and such that no master of our own time will be able to produce a better.

Michelangelo gazed at Galli with affection.

"You must have written this contract at home, rather than the bank."

"Why?"

"Because you have taken quite a gamble. Suppose when I finish the cardinal says, 'I have seen better marbles in Rome.' What happens then?"

"I give His Grace back his papal ducats."

"And you are stuck with the carving!"

Galli's eyes twinkled. "I could endure it."

He went searching the stoneyards of Trastevere and the ports for the kind of block he needed; but a seven-foot-wide, six-foot-tall, three-foot-deep cut of marble was rarely quarried on the chance of sale. It took him only two days to complete the rounds; there was nothing even faintly resembling the massive block he needed. The next day, when he had decided that he would have to go to Carrara at his own expense, Guffatti came running up the rear alley to his workshed, crying out:

". . . just unloaded a barge . . . the very size you're looking for. It was cut for some order in Lucca. The quarry never got paid, so they sold it."

He dog-trotted down to the Ripetta dock. There it stood, gleaming pure and white in the summer sun, beautifully cut by the quarrymen high in the mountains of Carrara. It tested out perfect against the hammer, against water, its crystals soft and compacted with fine graining. He came back before dawn the next morning, watched the rays of the rising sun strike the block and make it as transparent as pink alabaster, with not a hole or hollow or crack or knot to be seen in all its massive white weight.

His Pietà block had come home.

3.

He removed the last reminders of the Bacchus, settled down to the Pietà. But the Bacchus had become a controversial figure. Many people came to see it. Galli brought the visitors to the workshop or sent a servant to the shed to ask if Michelangelo would mind coming to the garden. He found himself plunged into explanations and defenses, particularly from the Bregno enthusiasts, who attacked it as "a perversion of the Dionysus legend." When there were admirers he found himself involved in describing his concept and technique. Galli wanted him for supper every night now, and Sundays, so that he could make as many friends as possible, open the way to more commissions.

The leading families of the Florentine community in Rome, the Rucellai, Cavalcanti, Altoviti were proud of him. They gave parties in his honor, from which he awoke the next morning feeling tired. He yearned to put the Bacchus behind him, to wipe the slate of his mind clean of the pagan carving and make the transition to the spirituality he needed to think about the Pietà. After a month of festivities it became clear that he was not going to be able to conceive or carve a Pietà under these diverting conditions; that with his emergence as a professional sculptor had come the time to establish his own quarters and workshop where he could live quietly, secluded, work night and day if he wished, dedicate himself to abstemiousness. He had grown up, he was on his own. He could see no other way.

Perceptive Jacopo Galli asked, "Something is troubling you, Michelangelo?"

"Yes."

"It sounds serious."

"Just ungrateful."

"You owe me nothing."

"The men to whom I owe the most have all said that: Lorenzo de' Medici, Bertoldo, Aldovrandi, and now you."

"Tell me what you want to do."

"To move out!" he blurted. "Life with the Galli family is too pleasant. . . ." He paused. "I feel the need to work in my own household. As a man, rather than a boy, and perennial guest. Does this sound foolish?"

Galli gazed at him wistfully. "I want only that you be happy, and that you carve the most beautiful marbles in Italy."

"For me they are one and the same."

He was directed to several houses in which the ground floor was available, one recommended by Altoviti in the Florentine quarter, another near the Piazza del Quirinale, with a fine view of Rome. They were too elaborate and expensive. On the third day, on the Via Sistina, across from the Bear Inn and on the edge of the Campo Marzio lying below the embankment of the Tiber, he found a big corner room with two windows, one facing north for steady light, the other east for the sharp sunlight he sometimes needed. At the rear was a smaller room with a fireplace. He paid a few scudi for two months' rent, drew up the oiled linen on wooden frames that served as window covering, and studied the shabby space: the wooden floor, thin in spots, broken in others, cement crumbling between the stones of the walls, the ceiling plaster falling in patches, exposing variegated colors of decay where the rain had leaked through. He put the key in his pocket and returned to the Galli's.

He found his brother Buonarroto waiting for him, jubilant. He had come as a guard on a mule train, and so the trip had cost him nothing. He was going back the same way. Michelangelo gazed with pleasure at the stubby features, the hair combed over Buonarroto's brow in imitation of his own. It had been a year since they had seen each other.

"You couldn't have come at a better time," he cried. "I need help in setting up my new home."

"You have taken a place? Good, then I can stay with you."

"Wait till you see my palatial quarters before you settle in," said Michelangelo, smiling. "Come with me to Trastevere, I need a supply of plaster, whitewash and lye. But first I will show you my Bacchus."

Buonarroto stood gazing at the statue a long time. Then he asked:

"Did people like it?"

"Most did."

"I'm glad."

That was all. Michelangelo observed to himself, "He doesn't have the faintest notion of what sculpture is about. His only interest is that people approve what I've done, so that I can be happy, and get more work . . . none of which he will ever understand. He's a true

Buonarroti, blind to the meaning of art. But he loves me."

They bought the supplies, had dinner at the Trattoria Toscana, then Michelangelo took his brother to the Via Sistina. When Buonarroto entered the room he whistled sharply.

"Michelangelo, surely you're not thinking of living in this . . . this hole? The place is falling apart."

"You and I are going to put it back together," replied Michelangelo grimly. "It is adequate work space."

"Father would be distressed."

Michelangelo smiled. "Don't tell him." He set a tall ladder in the center of the room. "Let's scrape this ceiling."

When they had scraped and given the ceiling a coat of plaster, they began on the walls, then set to work patching the broken floor with odd-sized pieces of wood. Next they turned their attention to the private courtyard. The only door to it was from the side of his room, but the other tenants had access from their windows, as a result of which it was covered with a thick compost of garbage and debris. The odor was as thick as the enclosing walls. It took two days to shovel the refuse into sacks and carry it through his own room to a vacant lot below the Tiber.

Balducci, who held all physical labor in abhorrence, showed up after Michelangelo and Buonarroto had finished their repairs. He knew a secondhand furniture dealer in Trastevere, where he bargained shrilly for the best prices on a bed, rope mattress, kitchen table, two cane chairs, chest of drawers, a few pots, dishes and knives. When the donkey cart arrived a few hours later, the brothers set up the bed under the window to the east, where Michelangelo would be waked at first light. The chest of drawers went on the back wall, next to the opening to the kitchen. Under the front north window he placed a table of four planks on horses, for his drawing, wax and clay modeling. The center of the big room he kept clear for his marble. In the rear cubicle they installed the kitchen table, two chairs, pots and dishes.

Buonarroto settled Michelangelo in, shopped and cooked the food, cleaned the rooms. The housekeeping went downhill the moment he left. Immersed in his work, Michelangelo took no time off to cook, to go out to a restaurant or eat in the streets. He lost weight, even as his rooms lost their tidy appearance. He saw nothing about him but his workbench and the huge white block sitting on beams in the center of the floor. He never bothered to make his bed or to wash the dishes he left on the kitchen table. The rooms became covered with dust from the street, ashes from the kitchen fire where he boiled water for an occasional hot drink. He knew by the end of a month that this system was not going to work.

Buonarroto solved his problem. Michelangelo answered to a knock late one afternoon to see standing in the street a plain-faced, olive-complected lad of about thirteen, travel-stained, holding out a letter on which Michelangelo recognized his brother's handwriting. The note introduced Piero Argiento, who had come to Florence looking for a sculptor to whom he could be apprenticed. He had been sent by someone to the Buonarroti house, then made the long trip on foot to Rome.

Michelangelo invited him in, studied the boy while he told of his family and their farm near Ferrara. His manner was quiet, his voice plain.

"Can you read and write, Argiento?"

"The Ingiesuati fathers in Ferrara taught me to write. Now I need to learn a trade."

"And you think sculpture might be a good one?"

"I want a three-year apprenticeship. With a Guild contract."

Michelangelo was impressed by the forthrightness. He gazed into the muddy brown eyes of the stringy lad before him, at the soiled shirt, wornout sandals, the thin, hungry cheeks.

"You have no friends in Rome? No place to go?"

"I came to see you." Stubbornly.

"I live simply, Argiento. You can expect no luxury."

"I am of *contadini*. What is to eat, we eat."

"Since you need a home, and I need a helper, suppose we try it for a few days? If it doesn't work out, we part as friends. I'll pay your way back to Florence."

"Agreed. *Grazie*."

"Take this coin, and go to the baths near Santa Maria dell'Anima. On the way back, stop at the market for food to cook."

"I make a good soup-of-the-country. My mother taught me before she died."

The fathers had taught Argiento not only to count but also to be doggedly honest. He left the house before dawn for the markets, carrying with him a scrap of crayon and paper. Michelangelo was touched by the way he painfully kept his accounts written down: so many denari for vegetables, so many for meat, for fruit, for bread and *pasta*, with every coin accounted for. Michelangelo put a modest amount in a cooking pot as their weekly allowance. Argiento was a relentless pursuer of bargains. Within a week he knew every stall selling produce. His shopping took him the better part of the morning, which suited Michelangelo because it gave him the solitariness he sought.

They established a simple routine. After their one-dish midday dinner, Argiento cleaned the rooms while Michelangelo took an hour's walk along the Tiber to the docks to listen to the Sicilians sing as they unloaded the boats. By the time he returned home Argiento was taking his *riposo* on the truckle bed in the kitchen under the wooden sink. Michelangelo had two more hours of quiet at his workbench before Argiento woke, washed his face noisily in a basin, and came to the worktable for his daily instruction. These few hours in the afternoon appeared to be all the teaching Argiento wanted. At dusk he was back in the kitchen, boiling water. By the time dark settled in he was asleep on his truckle bed, a blanket drawn securely over his head. Michelangelo then lit his oil lamps and returned to his workbench. He was grateful to Buonarroto for sending Argiento to him; the arrangement looked as though it would be satisfactory, despite the fact that Argiento showed not a shred of talent for drawing. Later, when he began working the marble, he would teach the boy how to use a hammer and chisel.

In the Bible he read from John 19:38–40:

After this Joseph of Arimathea, who was a disciple of Jesus . . . asked Pilate to let him take away the body of Jesus . . . so he came and took Jesus' body away; and with him was Nicodemus . . . he brought with him a mixture of myrrh and aloes, of about a hundred pounds' weight. They took Jesus' body, then, and wrapped it in winding-clothes with the spices; that is how the Jews prepare a body for burial.

Listed as present at the Descent were Mary, Mary's sister, Mary Magdalene, John, Joseph of Arimathea, Nicodemus. Search as he might, he could find no place where the Bible spoke of a moment when Mary could have been alone with Jesus. Mostly the scene was crowded with mourners, such as the dramatic Dell'Arca Lamentation in Bologna, where the grief-stricken spectators had usurped Mary's last poignant moment.

In his concept there could be no one else present.

His first desire was to create a mother and son alone in the universe. When might Mary have had that moment to hold her child on her lap? Perhaps after the soldiers had laid Him on the ground, while Joseph of Arimathea was at Pontius Pilate's asking for Christ's body, Nicodemus was gathering his mixture of myrrh and aloes, and the others had gone home to mourn. Those who saw his finished Pietà would take the place of the biblical witnesses. They would feel what Mary was undergoing. There would be no halos, no angels. These would be two human beings, whom God had chosen.

He felt close to Mary, having spent so long concentrating on the beginning of her journey. Now she was intensely alive, anguished; her Son was dead. Even though He would later be resurrected, He was at this moment dead indeed, the expression on His face reflecting what He had gone through on the cross. In his sculpture therefore it would not be possible for him to project anything of what Jesus felt for His mother; only what Mary felt for her Son. Jesus' inert body would be passive, His eyes closed. Mary would have to carry the human communication. This seemed right to him.

It was a relief to shift in his mind to technical problems. Since his Christ was to be life size, how was Mary to hold Him on her lap without the relationship seeming ungainly? His Mary would be slender of limb and delicate of proportion, yet she must hold this full-grown man as securely and convincingly as she would a child.

There was only one way to accomplish this: by design, by drawing diagrams and sketches in which he probed the remotest corner of his mind for creative ideas to carry his concept.

He started by making free sketches to loosen up his thinking so that images would appear on paper. Visually, these approximated what he was feeling within himself. At the same time he started walking the streets, peering at the people passing or shopping at the stalls, storing up fresh impressions of what they looked like, how they moved. In particular he sought the gentle, sweet-faced nuns, with head coverings and veils coming to the middle of their foreheads, remembering their expressions until he reached home and set them down on paper.

Discovering that draperies could be designed to serve structural purposes, he began a study of the anatomy of folds. He improvised as he went along, completing a life-size clay figure, then bought yards of an inexpensive material from a draper, wet the lightweight cloth in a basin and covered it over with clay that Argiento brought from the bank of the Tiber, to the consistency of thick mud. No fold could be accidental, each turn of the drapery had to serve organically, to cover the

Madonna's slender legs and feet so that they would give substantive support to Christ's body, to intensify her inner turmoil. When the cloth dried and stiffened, he saw what adjustments had to be made.

"So that's sculpture," commented Argiento wryly, when he had sluiced down the floor for a week, "making mud pies."

Michelangelo grinned. "See, Argiento, if you control the way these folds are bunched, like this, or made to flow, you can enrich the body attitudes. They can have as much tactile appeal as flesh and bone."

He went into the Jewish quarter, wanting to draw Hebraic faces so that he could reach a visual understanding of how Christ might have looked. The Jewish section was in Trastevere, near the Tiber at the church of San Francesco a Ripa. The colony had been small until the Spanish Inquisition of 1492 drove many Jews into Rome. Here, for the most part, they were well treated, as a "reminder of the Old Testament heritage of Christianity"; many of their gifted members were prominent in the Vatican as physicians, musicians, bankers.

The men did not object to his sketching them while they went about their work, but no one could be persuaded to come to his studio to pose. He was told to ask for Rabbi Melzi at the synagogue on Saturday afternoon. Michelangelo found the rabbi in the room of study, a gentle old man with a white beard and luminous gray eyes, robed in black gabardine with a skullcap on his head. He was reading from the Talmud with a group of men from his congregation. When Michelangelo explained why he had come, Rabbi Melzi replied gravely:

"The Bible forbids us to bow down to or to make graven images. That is why our creative people give their time to literature, not to painting or sculpture."

"But, Rabbi Melzi, you don't object to others creating works of art?"

"Not at all. Each religion has its own tenets."

"I am carving a Pietà from white Carrara marble. I wish to make Jesus an authentic Jew. I cannot accomplish this if you will not help me."

The rabbi said thoughtfully, "I would not want my people to get in trouble with the Church."

"I am working for the Cardinal of San Dionigi. I'm sure he would approve."

"What kind of models would you prefer?"

"Workmen. In their mid-thirties. Not bulky laborers, but sinewy men. With intelligence. And sensitivity."

Rabbi Melzi smiled at him with infinitely old but merry eyes.

"Leave me your address. I will send you the best the quarter has to offer."

Michelangelo hurried to Sangallo's solitary bachelor room with his sketches, asked the architect to design a stand which would simulate the seated Madonna. Sangallo studied the drawings and improvised a trestle couch. Michelangelo bought some scrap lumber. Together he and Argiento built the stand, covering it with blankets.

His first model arrived at dusk. He hesitated for a moment when Michelangelo asked him to disrobe, so Michelangelo gave him a piece of toweling to wrap around his loins, led him to the kitchen to take off his clothes. He then draped him over the rough stand, explained that he was supposed to be recently dead, and was being held on his mother's lap. The model quite plainly thought Michelangelo crazy; only the instructions from his rabbi kept him from bolting. But at the end of the sitting, when Michelangelo showed him the quick, free drawings, with the mother roughed in, holding her son, the model grasped what Michelangelo was after, and promised to speak to his friends. . . . He worked for two hours a day with each model sent by the rabbi.

Mary presented quite a different problem. Though this sculpture must take place thirty-three years after her moment of decision, he could not conceive of her as a woman in her mid-fifties, old, wrinkled, broken in body and face by labor or worry. His image of the Virgin had always been that of a young woman, even as had his memory of his mother.

Jacopo Galli introduced him into several Roman homes. Here he sketched, sitting in their flowing gowns of linen and silk, young girls not yet twenty, some about to be married, some married a year or two. Since the Santo Spirito hospital had taken only men, he had had no experience in the study of female anatomy; but he had sketched the women of Tuscany in their fields and homes. He was able to discern the body lines of the Roman women under their robes.

He spent concentrated weeks putting his two figures together: a Mary who would be young and sensitive, yet strong enough to hold her son on her lap; and a Jesus who, though lean, was strong even in death . . . a look he remembered well from his experience in the dead room of Santo Spirito. He drew toward the composite design from his meticulously accurate memory, without need to consult his sketches.

Soon he was ready to go into a three-dimensional figure in clay. Here he would have free expression because the material could be moved to distort forms. When he wanted to emphasize, or get greater intensity, he added or subtracted clay. Next he turned to wax because there was a similarity of wax to marble in tactile quality and translucence. He respected each of these approach techniques, and kept them in character: his quill drawings had a scratchiness, suggesting skin texture; the clay he used plastically to suggest soft moving flesh, as in an abdomen, in a reclining torso; the wax he smoothed over to give the body surface an elastic pull. Yet he never allowed these models to become fixed in his mind; they remained rough starting points. When carving he was charged with spontaneous energy; too careful or detailed studies in clay and wax would have glued him down to a mere enlarging of his model.

The true surge had to be inside the marble itself. Drawing and models were his thinking. Carving was action.

4.

The arrangement with Argiento was working well, except that sometimes Michelangelo could not figure who was master and who apprentice. Argiento had been trained so rigorously by the Ingiesuati that Michelangelo was unable to change his habits: up before dawn to scrub the floors, whether they were dirty or not; water boiling on the fire for washing laundry every day, the pots scoured with river sand after each meal.

"Argiento, this is senseless," he complained, not liking to work on the wet floors, particularly in cold weather. "You're too clean. Scrub the studio once a week. That's enough."

"No," said Argiento stolidly. "Every day. Before dawn. I was taught."

"And God help anyone who tries to unteach you!" grumbled Michelangelo; yet he knew that he had nothing to grumble about, for Argiento made few demands on him. The boy was becoming acquainted with the *contadini* families that brought produce into Rome. On Sundays he would walk miles into the *campagna* to visit with them, and in particular to see their horses. The one thing he missed from his farm in the Po Valley was the animals; frequently he would take his leave of Michelangelo by announcing:

"Today I go see the horses."

It took a piece of bad luck to show Michelangelo that the boy was devoted to him. He was crouched over his anvil in the courtyard getting his chisels into trim, when a splinter of steel flew into his eye and imbedded itself in his pupil. He stumbled into the house, eyes burning like fire. Argiento made him lie down on the bed, brought a pan of hot water, dipped some clean white linen cloth and applied it to extract the splinter. Though the pain was considerable Michelangelo was not too concerned. He assumed he could blink the splinter out. But it would not come. Argiento never left his side, keeping the water boiled, applying hot compresses throughout the night.

By the second day Michelangelo began to worry; and by the second night he was in a state of panic: he could see nothing out of the afflicted eye. At dawn Argiento went to Jacopo Galli. Galli arrived with his family surgeon, Maestro Lippi. The surgeon carried a cage of live pigeons. He told Argiento to take a bird out of the cage, cut a large vein under its wing, let the blood gush into Michelangelo's injured eye.

The surgeon came back at dusk, cut the vein of a second pigeon, again washed out the eye. All the next day Michelangelo could feel the splinter moving, pushing. By nightfall it was out.

Argiento had not slept for some seventy hours.

"You're tired," said Michelangelo. "Why don't you take a few days off?"

Argiento's stubborn features lit up with pleasure. "I go visit the horses."

At first Michelangelo had been bothered by the people going in and out of the Bear Hotel across the street, the noise of their horses and carts on the cobbles, the cries of the grooms and babble of a dozen dialects. By now he had grown to enjoy the interesting characters who came from all over Europe for their pilgrimage, some wearing long gowns, others short tunics of brilliant greens and purples, others stiff hats. They served as an unending source of models for him to sketch at his worktable as he saw them through the open window. Soon he came to know the clients; as a guest reappeared he quickly pulled out his drawing, made corrections or additions, caught the bodies in a variety of movements: unloading carriages, carrying valises, unshouldering packs, getting on and off mules.

The noise in the street, the voices, the welcomes, the departures gave him company without intruding upon his privacy. Living in isolation as he was, this sense of other people in the world was companionable. It was all he needed, for with marble in his hands he would never stand on the periphery looking in; he would stand at the focal core looking out.

In his pen and ink sketches for the Pietà he had crosshatched the negative spaces, those parts of the block that had to be thrown away, indicating the tool strokes that should be used. Now, with hammer and chisel in hand, he found this roughing out unpleasing, impatient for the first moment when a flicker of a buried image shone through, when the block became a source of life that communicated with him. Then, from the space outside the block, he entered into his composition. After he had completed the sculpture, life would vibrate outward from the figures. But at this beginning moment the action was in reverse: the point of entry must be a force that sucked in space, pulling inward his gaze and attention. He had envisaged so big a block because he wanted to sculpture with an abundance of marble. He did not want to have to compress any portion of his forms, as he had had to compact the Satyr close to the Bacchus.

He broke into his marble block at the left side of the Madonna's head, worked to the left of the block, the north light behind him. By getting Argiento to help him turn the block on its beams he was able to have the shadows fall exactly where the cavities were to be carved, a play of light and shadow to show him where he must cast out stone; for the marble he took away was also sculpture, creating its own effects.

Now he had to plunge in boldly to find his principal features. The weight of the material of the Madonna's head covering, forcing her head downward to the inner hand of Christ that crossed her heart, compelled attention to the body stretched across her lap. The tight band which ran between the Virgin's breasts was like a tight hand constricting and crushing a palpitating heart. The lines of the drapery led to the Madonna's hand, with which she held her Son, securely, under His arm, then to the human aspects of Christ's body, to His face, the eyes closed serenely in deep sleep, the nose straight but full, the skin clear and firm, the soft mustache and delicate curling chin whiskers, the mouth filled with anguish.

Because the Madonna was gazing down on her Son, all who looked must turn to her face, to see the sadness, the compassion for all men's sons, asking with tender despair: "What could I have done to save Him?" And from the depth of her love, "What purpose has all this served, if man cannot be saved?"

All who saw would feel how insupportably heavy was her Son's dead body on her lap, how much heavier was the burden in her heart.

It was unusual to combine two life-size figures in the same sculpture, revolutionary to put a full-grown man onto the lap of a woman. From this point of departure he left behind all conventional concepts of the Pietà. Once again, even as Ficino had believed that Plato could have been Christ's most loving disciple, it was Michelangelo's desire to blend the classical Greek concept of the beauty of the human body with the Christian ideal of the immortality of the human soul. He banished the lugubrious death throes of the earlier Pietàs, bathed his two figures in tranquillity. Human beauty could reveal sacredness as clearly as could pain. At the same time, it could exalt.

All of this, and much more, the marble must be persuaded to say. If the end result were tragic, then doubly must they walk in beauty; beauty that his own love and dedication could match in this flawless white block. He would make mistakes, but the mistakes would be made with loving hands.

Winter came down like a clap of thunder: cold, wet, raw. As Buonarroto had predicted, there were leaks. Michelangelo and Argiento moved his workbench and bed to dry sections of the room, brought the forge in from the courtyard. He wore his Bologna cap over his head and ears. His nostrils swelled, giving him constant pain, making breathing difficult.

He brought a black iron brazier to put under his work

stool, which warmed him posteriorly; but the moment he moved to another section of the room his blood froze. He had to send Argiento out for two more braziers, and baskets of coal, which they could hardly afford. When his fingers were blue he tried to carve while wearing woolen mittens. Within the hour he had an accident, some marble fell away and he felt his heart go down to his feet as the chunk hit the floor.

One Sunday Argiento returned from an outing feeling hot and strange. By midnight he had a high fever. Michelangelo picked him up off his truckle bed and put him into his own. By morning Argiento was in a delirium, sweating profusely, crying out names of relatives, fragments of stories, of beatings, accidents. Michelangelo wiped him dry, and a number of times had to restrain him from jumping out of bed.

At dawn he summoned a passer-by and sent him for a doctor. The doctor stood in the doorway, cried, "It's the plague! Burn everything he has touched since he came in here!" and fled.

Michelangelo sent a message to Galli. Maestro Lippi took one look, said scoffingly:

"Nonsense, it is not the plague. Quartan fever. Has he been around the Vatican lately?"

"He walked there on Sunday."

"And probably drank some stagnant water in the ditch beneath the walls. Go to the French monks on the Esquiline, they make a glutinous pill of sagepen, salt, coloquint . . ."

Michelangelo begged a neighbor to sit with Argiento. It took him almost an hour in the pelting rain to cross the city, go down the long street from Trajan's forum, past Augustus's forum and the basilica of Constantine,

the colosseum, then up the Esquiline hill to the monastery. The pills lessened Argiento's headache, and Michelangelo thought he was making good progress during two quiet days; then the delirium returned.

At the end of the week Michelangelo was exhausted.
He had brought Argiento's bed into the big room, and
was catching a few moments of sleep while Argiento
dozed, but worse than the lack of sleep was the problem of food, for he was unwilling to leave the boy
alone.

Balducci knocked on the door.

"You can't keep him here. You look like a skeleton.
Take him to the Santo Spirito hospital."

"And let him die?"

"Why should he die any faster at a hospital?"

"Because they don't get any care."

"What kind of care are you giving him, Dr.
Buonarroti?"

"I keep him clean, watch over him. . . . He took
care of me when I hurt my eye. How can I abandon
him to a ward? That's not Christian."

"If you insist on committing suicide, I'll bring you
food each morning before I go to the bank."

Michelangelo's eyes filled with gratitude. "Balducci,
you just play at being cynical. Here's some money, buy
me towels, and a sheet or two."

Michelangelo turned to find Argiento watching him.

"I'm going to die."

"No, you're not, Argiento. Nothing kills a country-
man but a falling cliff."

The illness took three weeks to pass. What hurt most
was the loss of almost a month of work; he began to

worry that he could not finish his statue within the stipulated year's time.

Winter was mercifully short in Rome. By March the *campagna* was flooded with a bright, brittle sunlight. The stones of the workshop began to thaw. And with the warmer weather came the Cardinal of San Dionigi to see how his Pietà was faring. Each time Michelangelo saw him there appeared to be more material and less body in his robes. He asked Michelangelo if he had been receiving his payments regularly. Michelangelo assured him that he had. They stood in front of the massive white block in the middle of the room. The figures were still rough, with much webbing left for support; but he had done considerable carving on the two faces, and that was what interested the cardinal most.

"Tell me, my son," he said softly, "how does the Madonna's face remain so young, younger than her Son's?"

"Your Grace, it seemed to me that the Virgin Mary would not age. She was pure; and so she would have kept her freshness of youth."

The answer was satisfactory to the cardinal.

"I hope you will finish in August. It is my dearest wish to hold services in St. Peter's for the installation."

5.

He carved in a fury from first light to dark, then threw himself across his bed, without supper and fully clothed, like a dead man. He awoke around midnight, refreshed, his mind seething with sculptural ideas, craving to get at the marble. He got up, nibbled at a heel of bread, lit the brass lamp in which he burned the dregs of the olive oil, and tried to set it at an angle that would throw light on the area he was carving. The light was too diffused. It was not safe to use a chisel.

He bought some heavy paper, made a hat with a peak, tied a wire around the outside and in the center fashioned a loop big enough to hold a candle. The light, as he held his face a few inches from the marble, was bright and steady. Nor did his pounding awaken Argiento under the kitchen sink, blanket over his head. The candles burned quickly, the soft wax running over the peak of his paper cap and onto his forehead, but he was delighted with his invention.

Late one night there was a sharp rap at the door. He opened it to find Leo Baglioni, who as emissary for Cardinal Riario di San Giorgio had brought Michelangelo to Rome. He was dressed in an indigo velvet cloak, surrounded by a group of his young friends who were holding horn lanterns or wax torches on long poles.

"I saw the light and came to see what you were doing at this ungodly hour. You're working! What's that stuff all over your eyebrows?"

Michelangelo proudly showed them his cap and candle. Leo and his friends burst into a paroxysm of laughter.

"Why don't you use goat's tallow, it's harder, you won't be eating it all night," exclaimed Leo, when he caught his breath.

Argiento disappeared the next day after supper, came back at the second hour of evening weighed down with four heavy bundles which he dumped on the bed.

"Signor Baglioni sent for me. These are a present."

Michelangelo extracted a hard yellow taper.

"I don't need his assistance!" he cried. "Take them back."

"They have broken my arm from the Campo dei Fiori. I won't carry them back. I'll set them in front of the door and burn them all at once."

"Very well, let me see if they are better than wax. But first I'll have to widen this wire loop."

Leo had known what he was talking about: the goat's tallow melted more slowly and remained in a pool where it fell.

He divided the night into two halves, one for sleep, the other for work, and made rapid progress carving the voluminous outer folds of Mary's robe, Christ's lower torso, His legs, the inner one raised so that it would be visible from the front, leaving a webbing connecting it with Mary's outstretched hand to protect it.

It was on a glorious summer morning with the air so translucent that the Alban hills seemed only a piazza away, that his cousin Paolo Rucellai sent for him to come as soon as possible. Michelangelo wondered what news it could be that Paolo considered urgent.

"Michelangelo, you look so thin."

"The sculpture grows fat, I grow thin. That is the natural order of things."

Rucellai regarded him in wonderment. "I had to tell you that on yesterday's post I received a letter from my cousin Bernardo. Florence is planning a sculpture competition."

Michelangelo's right hand began to tremble; he put his left hand over it to quiet it.

"To compete for what . . . ?"

"Bernardo's letter says: *To bring to perfection the marble column already blocked out by Agostino di Duccio, and now stored in the workshop of the cathedral.*"

"The Duccio block!"

"You know it?"

"I tried to buy it from the Signoria for my Hercules."

"That could be an advantage, if you remember it well."

"I can see it before my eyes as though it were lying at our feet in this room."

"Can you make something good of it?"

Michelangelo's eyes shone. "*Dio mio.*"

"My letter says the Council described the marble as 'badly blocked.'"

"No, no, it is a noble block. The original massing in the quarry was badly done, and Duccio dug in too deeply at the center . . ."

"Then you want to try for the competition?"

"More than anything in my whole life! Tell me, what must the theme be: political, religious? Is it for Florentine sculptors only? Must I be there to compete? Will they . . ."

"Whoa, whoa," cried Rucellai, "I have no further information. But I will ask Bernardo to send me full particulars."

"I'll come next Sunday to hear the news."

Rucellai laughed. "There won't be time for a reply, but come to dinner and we'll fatten you up for the competition."

"May I wait until you receive an answer?"

It took three weeks for Rucellai to summon him. Michelangelo sprinted up the steps to the library.

"Some news, not much. The date of the competition has not been set. It won't be until next year at the earliest. Themes can be submitted only by sculptors in Florence. . . ."

"I shall have to be back there."

"But the nature of the work has not yet been determined by the Council of the Wool Guild and the overseers of the cathedral."

"The cathedral? Then it will have to be a religious marble. After the Pietà, I was hoping to carve something different."

"The Wool Guild is paying, so I imagine the choice will be theirs. If I know these gentry, it will be a Florentine sculpture."

"Florentine? Like Marzocco?"

Rucellai chuckled at Michelangelo's dismay.

"No, not another lion. A symbol representing the new Republic, perhaps. . . ."

Michelangelo scratched his scalp in perplexity, using his fingers like a toothed chisel.

"What kind of statue would represent the Republic?"

"Perhaps that will be part of the competition? For the artist to tell them."

Paolo kept feeding him the news as it arrived over the Sabatini mountains from Florence: the competition would take place in 1500, to celebrate the hundredth anniversary of the competition for the Baptistery doors. The Wool Guild hoped that, like the Ghiberti, Brunelleschi and Della Quercia competition a century before, the Duccio block would attract sculptors from all over Italy.

"But this is already summer of '99. I have so much work left on the Pietà." His face was anguished. "I cannot rush, it is too important, too dear to me. Suppose I don't finish in time . . ."

Paolo put an arm about his trembling shoulders.

"I will bring you information steadily. The Wool Guild will debate through many meetings and many months before they set the terms."

It was the Cardinal of San Dionigi who lost the race with time. His Grace never did get to see his sculpture completed, though he sent the last hundred ducats to Galli's bank at the beginning of August, when the sculpture was to have been installed. The cardinal died quietly in the midst of his offices. Jacopo Galli attended the funeral with Michelangelo, standing below a catafalque sixteen feet long between the columns of the church, and nine feet wide, with singers behind the main altar. Returning to the Galli home, Michelangelo asked:

"Who decides whether or not the Pietà is 'more beautiful than any work in marble to be seen in Rome to-day'?"

"The cardinal already decided that. After his visit with you in May. He said you were fulfilling the contract. That's good enough for me. When do you think it will be finished?"

"I have still six to eight months of work."

"In time for the Centennial Year, then. That will give you an audience from all over Europe."

Michelangelo shifted uneasily in his seat.

"Would you send that last hundred ducats to my family? They are in some kind of trouble again."

Galli looked at him sharply. "That was your last payment. You say you have six to eight months of work left, and I have sent almost all of the cardinal's ducats to Florence. It begins to look like a bottomless well."

"This money I want to invest in buying a shop for my brothers, Buonarroto and Giovansimone. Buonarroto cannot seem to find a place for himself. Giovansimone, since Savonarola's death, takes jobs, then disappears for days. If they could find a good shop, and I shared in the profits . . ."

"Michelangelo, if neither of them is a good businessman, how are they going to make a profit?" Galli was exasperated; but when he spoke again his voice was solicitous. "I can't let you pour your last money down a hole. You must be practical and protect yourself against the future. Eighty per cent of your money from the Bacchus and the Pietà has gone to your family. I ought to know, I'm your banker."

Michelangelo hung his head, whispered, "Buonarroto won't work for anyone else, so I must set him up in business. And if I don't get Giovansimone in a straight path now, I may never have another chance."

The money was transferred to Florence, Michelangelo keeping a few ducats for himself. At once, he began to need things: equipment for his carving, utensils for the house, clothes for himself and Argiento. He went on short rations, gave Argiento money for nothing but the simplest foods. Their clothing became ragged. It took a letter from Lodovico to bring him to his senses.

Dearest Son:
Buonarroto tells me that you live there in great misery. Misery is bad, since it is a vice displeasing to God and to one's fellow man, and also will hurt the soul and the body. . . . Live moderately and mind not to be in need, and abstain from discomfort. . . . Above all, take care of your head, keep it moderately warm and never wash yourself. Allow yourself to be rubbed, but do not wash yourself.

He went to Paolo Rucellai, borrowed twenty-five florins, took Argiento to the Trattoria Toscana for *bistecca alla fiorentina*. On the way home he bought himself and Argiento each a new shirt, a pair of long hose and sandals.

6.

It was his task to impregnate the marble with manifest spirit; yet even in a religious theme he felt deeply for the whole man, alive to every nerve, muscle, vein, bone, to the skin and hair, fingers, eyes and mouth. All must come alive if he were to create power and monumentality by incorporating into the marble the strength of man. He carved upward, using his knowledge of the forms already released below, and an intuition as old and deep as the long-buried marble, to achieve the expression for Mary that emerged not only from her emotion but from the feeling of the whole sculpture. He stood with his head lower than Mary's, his hands opposite his forehead, the tools angled upward, carving as close as he could get to the drama of the Pietà. The block saw him face to face, the sculptor and the sculptured involved in the tender restrained sadness. He left far behind him the dark, unforgiving Pietàs, their message of love blotted out by blood. He would not sculpture agony. The nail holes in Christ's hands and feet were tiny dots. There was no sign of violence. Jesus slept peacefully in His mother's arms. Over the two figures there was a suffusion, a luminosity. His Christ awakened the deepest sympathy, not abhorrence for those who stood outside the sculpture and had been responsible.

His religious faith he projected in terms of the sublimity of the figures; the harmony between them was his way of portraying the harmony of God's universe. He did not attempt to make Christ divine, since he would not have known how, but exquisitely human. The Virgin's head emerged delicate, the features Florentine, the face of a maiden with silent pale composure. In her expression he made a distinction between divine and sublime; sublime, for him, meant supreme and perfect. He reflected, "The meaning of the figures lies in their human qualities; the beauty of face and form portrays the grandeur of their spirit."

He found that he was achieving a tactile richness, with the forms mirroring the loving days he had devoted to them.

Balducci brought him the news that Sansovino, his fellow apprentice in the Medici garden, had returned to Florence after working for a number of years in Portugal, and been commissioned to do a marble group of St. John Baptizing Christ for the Baptistery. He was looked upon as the logical choice to win the Duccio block commission.

"Sansovino is a good sculptor," said Michelangelo loyally.

"Better than you?"

He swallowed hard before he replied. "He finishes well everything he starts."

"Do you think he can win over you?"

Again Michelangelo struggled with his answer. "We both will do our best."

"I've never seen you modest before."

Michelangelo blushed. He was grimly determined to outdesign Sansovino and win the contest; but he would not talk Sansovino down.

"Leo Baglioni tells me I have few friends. Sansovino is a friend. I intend to keep him."

"Torrigiani is also entering the competition, and is telling everyone that he will get the Duccio marble because he was an anti-Medici man; and that, since you backed Piero, you won't be allowed to compete. Paolo Rucellai says you must return to Florence in time to make your peace with the Signoria."

This intelligence cost him several nights of sleep. He had occasion to bless Baglioni for his generous supply of goat tallow candles.

In mid-January snow began to fall, and fell heavily for two days, accompanied by wind from the north. The piercing cold lasted for several weeks. Michelangelo's enclosed courtyard was piled high with snow. Inside the rooms were frigid. There was no way to keep the icy boreal wind from coming in through the wood and linen shutters. The three braziers made no impression. Michelangelo worked with his hat and earmuffs on, and a blanket pinned around his shoulders. Again in February the snow and ice came. The city was still, the markets abandoned, the shops closed because the ice, sleet and frozen mud made the streets impassable.

Michelangelo and Argiento suffered. Michelangelo took the boy into bed with him to combine their warmth. Damp oozed through the whitewash on the walls. The leaks were slower under the compacted snow, but lasted longer. Coal was in short supply, the price went up so heavily that Michelangelo could buy only a minimum amount. Argiento spent hours scratching in the snow of the surrounding fields looking for wood for his fire.

Michelangelo caught cold, went down with fever. Argiento found two bricks at an interrupted building job, heated them in his fire, wrapped them in towels and alternated them on Michelangelo's feet to keep down the chill. He fed him hot beef broth. No work was done; for how many days Michelangelo lost count. Fortunately there remained only the polishing. He did not have the strength for the heavy manual labor involved in the cutting.

For his Pietà he hoped to achieve the highest polish of which marble was capable, a faultless velvety loftiness. On the first warm day he walked to Trastevere and bought several large lumps of pumice, divided them with a blow of the hammer, searching for flatter surfaces. Now he could grip the pieces in the palm of his hand, using the long, silky parallel strands to polish the broad planes of the Madonna's robe, of Christ's chest and legs: slowly, with infinite patience, over long days and weeks.

Now he needed sharper edges, split the pumice with his chisel, cut the appropriate shapes to reach into the recessions, cavities and undulations of hair, cloth, fingernails. Finally, he made sharp-edged slivers that looked like primitive arrowheads to polish the curves around Christ's nostrils. He did not finish the back of Mary since the statue was to sit in a niche, but left the marble lined and blocked, as were the rough rocks on which she was sitting. The white marble, polished and gleaming, lighted up the dingy room as though it were a stained-glass chapel. The homely artist had indeed created a work of beauty.

Giuliano da Sangallo, Michelangelo's old friend from Florence and the first man to instruct him in the art of architecture, was the first to see the finished sculpture. He made no comment on the religious aspect of the marble, but congratulated Michelangelo on the architecture of the triangular composition, the balance of lines and masses.

Jacopo Galli came to the studio and studied the Pietà in silence. After a time he said softly, "I have fulfilled my contract with the Cardinal of San Dionigi: this is the most beautiful work in marble to be seen in Rome today."

"I'm nervous about the installation," said Michelangelo. "Our contract doesn't say that we have the right to put the Pietà in St. Peter's. With the cardinal dead . . ."

"We won't ask any questions. We'll install it without a sound. What no one knows, no one can object to."

Michelangelo was aghast. "You mean, sneak my sculpture in?"

"Nothing furtive. Just discreet. Once the Pietà is sitting in its niche, no one will bother to have it removed."

"But the Pope was fond of the cardinal. He gave him a three-day funeral. He granted him permission to put a sculpture in the Chapel of the Kings. Why should anyone want to have it removed?"

"I'm sure they won't," said Galli reassuringly. "Suppose you hire those stoneyard friends of yours to help you. Tomorrow, after dinner, while the city is resting."

There were so many obtruding parts: hands, feet, folds, that he did not dare to entrust the moving of the marble to beams or crowbars, no matter how securely he wrapped it. He asked Guffatti, the owner of the stone-yard in Trastevere who had transported the precious white Carrara marble block Michelangelo had transformed into the Bacchus, to come to the workshop, showed him the Pietà and discussed the problem with him. Guffatti stood in front of the sculpture in silence, then said:

"I bring the family."

The family turned out to include not merely three husky sons but a variety of cousins. They would not allow Michelangelo to touch the piece, wrapping it in a half dozen mangy blankets and then, accompanied by a medley of cries, arguments and commands, lifting it on its base. They carried the Pietà, eight strong, to the ancient wagon with its bed of straw, and roped it in. With Michelangelo guarding the tailgate, they made their way cautiously along the cobbled Via Posterula, across the Sant'Angelo bridge, then down the newly opened, smooth Via Alessandrina, which the Pope had rebuilt to celebrate the Centennial Year. For the first time since he had come to Rome, Michelangelo had occasion to bless the Borgia.

The Guffatti stopped their wagon at the foot of the thirty-five steps. Only the fact that they were under a sacred burden kept them from cursing as they carried the heavy marble up the first three sections of seven steps, set it down to rest and wipe the perspiration from their brows, then picked it up again to carry to the atrium, past the splashing fountain and to the church door.

Here, while the Guffatti stopped once more to rest, Michelangelo had a chance to observe that the basilica was leaning even more sharply than when he had begun work. It was now so dilapidated it seemed beyond repair. He swallowed hard at the thought of putting his lovely Pietà in a basilica which had not long to remain upright. Surely the first wind to roar down off the Alban hills would flatten it? He had an image of himself crawling over the rubble to find the fragments of his shattered statue, was reassured only when he remembered Sangallo's architectural drawings which showed how St. Peter's could be counterpropped.

The Guffatti once again picked up the load. Michelangelo led them into the basilica, with its five corresponding naves and hundreds of columns assembled from all over Rome; then into the Chapel of the Kings of France, to the left of a huge figure of Christ enthroned. The Guffatti lowered their bundle carefully before the empty niche, unwrapped the blankets, wiped their hands clean of sweat, raised the Pietà reverentially to its place. Michelangelo straightened it to the position he wanted. The Guffatti family bought candles from an old woman in black, lit them before the statue.

They refused to take one scudo for their hours of backbreaking labor.

"We take our pay in heaven," said the father.

It was the best tribute Michelangelo could receive. It was also the only tribute he received.

Jacopo Galli came into the chapel, accompanied by Balducci. His head bobbed with pleasure. Guffatti, standing amidst his relatives, asked: "Is this all? No services? No blessing by the priest?"

Galli answered, "It was blessed in the carving."

The Guffatti and Argiento knelt before the Virgin, crossed themselves, murmured a prayer. Michelangelo gazed up at the Pietà, feeling sad and depleted. As he reached the door of the chapel and turned back for a last look, he saw that the Virgin too was sad and lonely; the most alone human being God ever put on earth.

He returned to St. Peter's day after day. Few of the city's pilgrims bothered to visit the Chapel of the Kings of France. Those who did hastily genuflected before the Pietà, crossed themselves and moved on.

Because Galli had advised discretion, few in Rome knew the statue had been installed. Michelangelo could get no reaction. Paolo Rucellai, Sangallo, Cavalcanti visited St. Peter's; the rest of the Florentine colony, grieved over the execution of Savonarola, refused to go inside the Vatican walls.

After nearly two years of dedicated work, Michelangelo sat in his cheerless room, now empty, despondent. No one came to speak of sculpture. He was so exhausted that he could not even think of the Duccio block. Nor did Galli believe this the appropriate time to cry up a new job for him.

One afternoon he wandered into St. Peter's, saw a family with several grown children, from Lombardy, he guessed by their clothes and dialect, standing in front of his Pietà, making elaborate gestures of the hands. He went to their side to eavesdrop.

"I tell you I recognize the work," cried the mother of the family. "It is by that fellow from Osteno, who makes all the tombstones."

Her husband waved the fingers of both his hands loosely, shaking off this idea as a dog shakes off water.

"No, no, it is one of our countrymen, Cristoforo Solari, called 'The Hunchback,' from Milan. He has done many of them."

That night Michelangelo made his way through the streets, green sailcloth bag in hand. He entered St. Peter's, took a candle from the bag, put it in the wire loop of his hat, reached into the bag again for hammer and chisel. He raised his tools, leaned forward across the Christ so that the candle cast a steady glow on the Virgin's bosom. Onto the band going tightly between the breasts he cut in swift, decorative letters:

MICHAEL·ÂGLVS·BONAROVS·FLOEN·FACEBAT

Michelangelo Buonarroti of Florence made this.

EPILOGUE

The old basilica of St. Peter's, begun in 324 by Constantine and embracing the Chapel of the Kings of France, leaned heavily to one side, in severe danger of collapsing. In 1506, Pope Julius II decided to take down the ancient basilica, but to embrace as much of the old as possible inside a new St. Peter's. However, it was not until 1537 that the Pietà was removed to a safe niche in the Chapel of the Virgin Mary of the Fever.

It appears to have remained there until after Michelangelo's death, and after a considerable part of the new St. Peter's was completed. Pope Gregory XIII moved it again sometime between 1572 and 1585, to the choir of Sixtus IV. Here it remained for about 170 years, when it was moved for a third time, to the Chapel of the Pietà. The journey to New York is its fourth journey in the 464 years since Michelangelo and his stonecarver friends carried it secretly into the old basilica.

Before his death, Michelangelo had the gratification of seeing the Pietà accepted and revered. It is highly likely that it will be accepted and revered by the many Americans who will see it displayed in the Vatican Pavilion at the New York World's Fair. It may also have a profound effect upon them, an effect of emotional, artistic and spiritual intensity rarely aroused by a single work of art. It is not too much to say, as the late Bernard Berenson did:

"The impact of a great work of art can enlarge and deepen a person's perspective on life."